EASY ALKALINE DIET RECIPES FOR BEGINNERS

Maintain PH Level, Keep Your Body in Alkaline State, and Stay Healthy and Lean with This Essential Guide of Alkaline Diet with Many Delicious and Nutritious recipes.

BY

Salena Doyle

Table of Contents

INTRODUCTION

The alkaline diet, likewise called the alkaline debris diet or alkaline corrosive diet, was made mainstream by its big name devotees. Enormous names like Victoria Beckham, Jennifer Aniston, and Kate Hudson have said they attempted the diet with positive results.the reason of the alkaline diet is that the food varieties you eat can change your body's pH. Advertisers of the diet accept that by eating food varieties that are not so much acidic but rather more alkaline, you'll be shielded from a few medical problems.

Corrosive Ash Hypothesis

The diet fixates on the unproven corrosive debris theory, which basically says devouring a diet wealthy in foods grown from the ground and with moderate measures of protein advances an alkaline burden and a better way of life. (1)

How Does the Plan Work?

The alkaline diet underscores burning-through alkaline food sources trying to make the body's pH more alkaline. All things considered, it is difficult to change the body's pH through diet. For sure, the body's pH really changes dependent on the locale. For instance, the stomach is more acidic. (More on this later.)

Regardless, the proportion of pH discloses to you how acidic or alkaline something is and goes from 0 to 14.

Easy alkaline diet recipes 25+ recipes

1.   Tofu scramble

Prep:10 mins Cook:20 mins Easy Serves 2

Ingredients:

- 1 tbsp olive oil
- 1 little onion , finely cut
- 1 large garlic clove , squashed
- ½ tsp turmeric
- 1 tsp ground cumin
- ½ tsp sweet smoked paprika
- 280g additional firm tofu
- 100g cherry tomatoes , split
- ½ little pack parsley , chopped
- rye bread , to serve, (optional)

Strategy:

1. Heat the oil in a skillet over a medium heat and delicately fry the onion for 8 - 10 mins or until brilliant brown and tacky. Mix in the garlic, turmeric, cumin and paprika and cook for 1 min.

2. Generally crush the tofu in a bowl using a fork, keeping a few pieces stout. Add to the skillet and fry for 3 mins. Raise the heat, at that point tip in the tomatoes, cooking for 5 mins more or until they start to relax. Crease the parsley through the blend. Serve all alone or with toasted rye bread (not sans gluten), in the event that you like.

2.   Sweet & sour tofu

Prep:10 mins Cook:15 mins Easy Serves 1

Ingredients:

- 1 tbsp rapeseed or vegetable oil
- 75g extra-firm tofu , cut into 2cm pieces
- ½ onion , cut into slight wedges
- ½ red pepper , chopped into lumps
- 1 large garlic clove , finely cut
- 80g new pineapple lumps
- 1 tbsp low-salt ketchup
- 1 tbsp rice wine vinegar
- ½ tbsp dim soy sauce
- cooked basmati rice , to serve
- sesame seeds , to serve

Technique:

1. Heat a large portion of the oil in a non-stick griddle over a medium heat. Add the tofu and

fry for 5 mins, turning routinely, until brilliant brown on all sides. Eliminate to a plate with an opened spoon and put away.

2. Heat the excess oil in the dish over a high heat. Fry the onion, pepper and garlic for 5-6 mins, or until the veg starts to relax. Add the pineapple, ketchup, vinegar, soy sauce and 50ml water, and stew for 1 min, or until somewhat diminished. Mix the tofu back into the dish.

3. Cook the basmati rice adhering to pack guidelines. Serve the tofu in bowls with the rice and a sprinkling of sesame seeds.

3.   Crispy tofu

Prep:5 mins Cook:10 mins plus 20 mins draining Easy Serves 2-4

Ingredients:

- 400g square firm tofu
- 3 tbsp cornflour
- ½ tsp garlic granules
- ½ tsp smoked paprika
- ½ tsp fine ocean salt
- ½ tsp ground dark pepper
- 2 tbsp vegetable oil

Strategy:

1. Channel the tofu, enclose by 4-5 sheets of kitchen paper, put on a plate and put something substantial over the top, similar to a wooden cleaving load up, or a plate with a

couple of tins on it. Leave for 20 mins to empty the abundance dampness out of the tofu.

2. Blend the cornflour, garlic, paprika, salt and pepper in a little bowl. Disentangle the tofu from the paper, cut down the middle through the middle, at that point cut into triangles, 3D squares or strips.

3. Throw the tofu pieces in the spiced cornflour to cover all finished. Heat the oil in a large non-stick griddle over a medium-high heat. Fry the tofu for 2-4 mins on each side until brilliant, crunchy and browned at the edges. More modest 3D squares will take 2 mins each side, larger triangles will take 4 mins. Cook in clusters on the off chance that you need to, adding somewhat more oil if the container gets dry.

4. Channel the cooked tofu on kitchen paper and season with a squeeze more salt prior to serving.

4. Tofu & spinach cannelloni

Prep:25 mins Cook:1 hr Easy Serves 6

Ingredients:

- 2 tbsp olive oil
- 1 onion , chopped
- 3 garlic cloves , finely chopped
- 2 x 400g jars chopped tomatoes
- 50g pine nuts , generally chopped
- 400g pack spinach
- squeeze ground nutmeg
- 349g pack luxurious tofu
- 300g pack new lasagne sheets
- 4 tbsp new breadcrumbs

Technique:

1. Heat a large portion of the oil in a container, add onion and 1/3 of the garlic and fry for 4

mins until softened. Pour in tomatoes, prepare and bring to the bubble. Decrease heat and cook for 10 mins until sauce thickens.

2. Heat half excess oil in a griddle and cook another 1/3 of garlic for 1 min, at that point add a large portion of the pine nuts and the spinach. Shrivel spinach, at that point tip out overabundance fluid. Whizz tofu in a food processor or with a hand blender until smooth, at that point mix through the spinach with the nutmeg and some pepper. Eliminate from the heat; permit to cool marginally.

3. Heat oven to 200C/180C fan/gas 6. Empty half pureed tomatoes into a 20 x 30cm dish. Gap spinach blend between lasagne sheets, move up and lay on top of sauce. Pour over leftover sauce. Prepare for 30 mins.

4. Blend morsels in with residual garlic and pine nuts. Sprinkle over top of dish, shower with outstanding oil and prepare for 10 mins until scraps are brilliant.

Formula TIPS

4 REASONS TO EAT TOFU

Wealthy in protein • Low fat • Helps to bring down cholesterol • Can calm menopausal indications

5. Slow-cooker vegetable lasagna

Prep:30 mins Cook:2 hrs and 30 mins - 3 hrs

Easy Serves 4

Ingredients:

- 1 tbsp rapeseed oil
- 2 onions, cut
- 2 large garlic cloves, chopped
- 2 large courgettes, diced (400g)
- 1 red and 1 yellow pepper, deseeded and generally cut
- 400g can chopped tomatoes
- 2 tbsp tomato purée
- 2 tsp vegetable bouillon
- 15g new basil, chopped in addition to a couple of leaves
- 1 large aubergine, cut across length or width for greatest surface territory

- 6 wholewheat lasagne sheets (105g)
- 125g vegan wild ox mozzarella, chopped

Technique:

1. Heat 1 tbsp rapeseed oil in a large non-stick skillet and fry 2 cut onions and 2 chopped large garlic cloves for 5 mins, blending as often as possible until softened.

2. Tip in 2 diced large courgettes, 1 red and 1 yellow pepper, both generally cut, and 400g chopped tomatoes with 2 tbsp tomato purée, 2 tsp vegetable bouillon and 15g chopped basil.

3. Mix well, cover and cook for 5 mins. Try not to be enticed to add more fluid as a lot of dampness will come from the vegetables once they begin cooking.

4. Cut 1 large aubergine. Lay a large portion of the cuts of aubergine in the foundation of the lethargic cooker and top with 3 sheets of lasagne.

5. Add 33% of the ratatouille combination, at that point the leftover aubergine cuts, 3 more lasagne sheets, at that point the excess ratatouille blend.

6. Cover and cook on High for 2½ - 3 hours until the pasta and vegetables are delicate. Mood killer the machine.
7. Dissipate 125g veggie lover bison mozzarella over the vegetables at that point cover and leave for 10 mins to settle and soften the cheddar.
8. Dissipate with additional basil and present with a modest bunch of rocket.

6. Vegetable gyoza

Preparation and cooking time Prep:2 hrs Cook:20 mins plus 1 hr chilling Makes 25

Ingredients:

- 250g plain flour
- cornflour, for cleaning
- For the filling
- 200g white cabbage
- 4 chestnut mushrooms
- 1 carrot
- 4 water chestnuts (optional)
- thumb-sized piece of ginger, stripped and finely ground
- 2 garlic cloves, finely ground
- 3 spring onions, finely cut
- 2 tbsp sunflower oil, in addition to extra for searing

- 1 tbsp soy sauce
- 1 tbsp saké, Shaohsing rice wine or dry sherry
- For the plunging sauce
- 6 tbsp soy sauce
- 2 tbsp rice wine vinegar
- firm stew oil (optional)

Strategy:

1. In case you're making your own batter, tip the flour and 1 tsp salt into a bowl. Carry a pot to the bubble and measure 150ml bubbling water. Gradually pour the water over the flour while blending in with a spoon to shape a firm batter. At the point when the mixture is sufficiently cool to deal with, tip onto a surface and ply for 10 mins until smooth. Wrap the batter and chill for at any rate 1 hr. On the other hand, you can utilize 25-30 shop-purchased gyoza skins.

2. In the interim, coarsely grind the cabbage, mushrooms, carrot and water chestnuts, in the event that using, tip into a bowl. Add the ginger, garlic and spring onions. Heat the oil in a wok, at that point tip in all the veg and pan fried food over a high heat for 3 mins until

softened. Sprinkle over the soy sauce and purpose, and cook for 2-3 mins. Season to taste. Tip once again into the bowl to cool totally.

3. Separation the batter in two. Disperse a surface liberally with cornflour and carry one wad of batter out until paper-meager. Utilize a 10cm shaper to remove rounds of mixture and heap them up (they will not stick due to the cornflour). Rehash with all the batter, re-rolling the decorations until you have around 25 skins.

4. To gather, sprinkle cornflour on a plate and have a bowl of cold water prepared. Hold a skin in the palm of one hand and put a teaspoon of the filling in the middle. Plunge your finger in the water and wipe around within edge of the skin. Bring the edges of the skin together, squeezing creases along one side. Space them out on a heating plate and freeze, at that point tip into a sack and set back in the cooler. Will save for a quarter of a year. Can be cooked from frozen.

5. Heat a sprinkle of oil in a non-leave griddle with a cover. Fry, level side down, for 2 mins

until brilliant. Add 100ml water to the skillet and cover. Cook over a medium heat for 3-5 mins until the water has dissipated and the gyoza is cooked through. Eliminate the cover and leave the gyoza to sizzle on the base briefly. Combine the plunging sauce ingredients as one, at that point present with the gyoza.

7.   Easy green vegetable soup

Prep:10 mins Cook:15 mins Easy Serves 6
Ingredients:
- 1bunch spring onions, chopped
- 1large potato, stripped and chopped
- 1 garlic clove, squashed
- 1l vegetable stock
- 250g frozen peas
- 100g new spinach
- 300ml normal yogurt
- scarcely any mint leaves, basil leaves, cress or a combination, to serve

Strategy:
1. Put the spring onions, potato and garlic into a large dish. Pour over the vegetable stock and bring to the bubble.
2. Diminish the heat and stew for 15 mins with a cover on or until the potato is adequately delicate to pound with the rear of a spoon.

3. Add the peas and bring back up to a stew. Scoop out around 4 tbsp of the peas and put away for the embellishment.
4. Mix the spinach and yogurt into the skillet, at that point cautiously empty the entire combination into a blender or utilize a stick blender to barrage it until it's actual smooth. Season to taste with dark pepper.
5. Scoop into bowls, at that point add a portion of the held cooked peas and dissipate over your number one delicate spices or cress. Present with dried up bread, on the off chance that you like.

8.   Double cheese & spring vegetable tart

Preparation and cooking time Prep:30 mins Cook:1 hr Easy Serves 8

Ingredients:
- 500g square shortcrust baked good
- plain flour , for tidying
- 25g develop cheddar , finely ground
- 200g asparagus lances , woody finishes managed
- 100g new podded or frozen peas
- 2 eggs
- 100g crème fraîche
- 150g twofold cream
- entire nutmeg , for grinding
- 100g watercress
- 300g or 2 logs of delicate, rindless goat's cheddar

Strategy:
1. Carry the cake out into a square shape on a work surface delicately cleaned with flour. Dissipate over the cheddar, overlap the cake down the middle and carry out again into a circle that fits a 25cm tart tin with a shade.

Chill for 20 mins. In the mean time, cook the asparagus in bubbling water for 3 mins, at that point deplete and invigorate under cool water. Cook the new peas a similar path briefly, or just thaw out the frozen peas.

2. Heat oven to 200C/180C fan/gas 6. Prick the foundation of the tart well with a fork, line with heating material and load up with preparing beans. Prepare the tart for 30 mins, eliminate the material and beans, prick again assuming it has puffed up, heat for another 10-15 mins until roll brown.

3. In the interim, beat the eggs in a bowl, add the crème fraîche and cream, season and add a touch of newly ground nutmeg. Dissipate the peas and the majority of the watercress over the tart and disintegrate over a large portion of the goat's cheddar. Pour over the rich egg combination, at that point lay the asparagus lances on top. At last, cut the excess goat's cheddar and mastermind on top, at that point heat for 25-30 mins until the custard is simply set and the cheddar is brilliant brown. Leave to cool in the tin, trim the edges of the baked good, at that point eliminate from the tin, dissipate with the excess watercress and serve cut into cuts. Can be made as long as a day ahead, leave out the refrigerator to keep the baked good fresh.

Formula TIPS

CHANGE UP THE PASTRY

Collapsing ingredients through shop-purchased baked good is an incredible method to redo it. Rather than cheddar, other ground hard cheeses like parmesan would work, just as new thyme leaves, finely chopped rosemary or some dark onion or poppy seeds.

Works out positively For

Spring sheep sticks with delicately cured portion salad

Jam and custard trifle squares

Broiled new carrots, cauliflower, grains and carrot-top dressing

9. Vegetable biryani with green raita

Prep:10 mins Cook:30 mins Easy Serves 2 (easily doubled)

Ingredients:

- 100g wholemeal basmati rice
- 2 tsp rapeseed oil
- 1 large onion, split and cut (200g)
- 2 carrots, cut into little dice (160g)
- 200g cauliflower, cut into scaled down pieces
- 2 tbsp medium curry powder
- 1 cinnamon stick, snapped fifty-fifty
- 1 tsp cumin seeds
- 1 tbsp finely ground ginger
- 3 large garlic cloves, finely ground
- 150g pot bio yogurt
- 2 tsp vegetable bouillon powder
- 25g simmered cashews (not salted)
- 160g frozen peas
- modest bunch of mint, finely chopped
- 2 modest bunches of new coriander, finely chopped

Technique:

1. Tip the rice into a skillet of bubbling water and cook for 12 mins until just half cooked. Channel, yet hold the water. In the mean time, heat the oil in a large non-stick dish that suffers a heart attack, and fry the onion over a medium heat until brilliant. In the event that it begins to get, cover with the top.
2. Tip in the carrots and cauliflower, and keep cooking, covered, for 5 mins. Mix in the curry powder, cinnamon and cumin seeds, the ginger and garlic. Mix well. Tip in the rice, add 2 tbsp of the yogurt and pour in 300ml of the held rice water blended in with the bouillon powder. Mix in the cashews and peas. Cover and cook for 10 mins over a delicate heat until the rice is delicate and all the fluid has been retained. Add a large portion of the mint and a large portion of the coriander, at that point leave to rest for 5 mins.
3. In the interim, make a raita by mixing the excess mint and coriander into the leftover yogurt, at that point add 1 tbsp cold water to relax – you can whizz along with a hand blender on the off chance that you need a green raita. Spoon into little dishes to serve close by the biryani.

10. Root vegetable tatin with candied nuts & blue cheese

Prep:25 mins Cook:50 mins - 55 mins Easy Serves 6

Ingredients:

- 500g square puff cake
- 3 thin carrots, around 12-13 cm since a long time ago, split lengthways
- 3 thin parsnips around 12-13 cm since a long time ago, split lengthways in addition to 1 large parsnip, stripped and ground
- 2 tbsp olive oil
- 2 piled tbsp somewhat salted spread
- 5 banana shallots, 3 split lengthways, 2 daintily cut
- little pack sage, leaves picked and finely chopped
- 4 rosemary twigs, leaves picked and finely chopped
- 2 garlic cloves, finely ground or squashed
- 100g caster sugar
- 125ml red wine vinegar

- 100g blue cheddar, disintegrated (we utilized Cropwell Bishop)
- For the sweetened nuts

- 50g pecans, generally chopped
- 25g caster sugar
- 2 tsp spread
- 3 rosemary twigs

Strategy:

1. Heat oven to 200C/180C fan/gas 6. Carry out the cake to only larger than a 30cm distance across ovenproof skillet and utilize the dish as a layout to remove a series of cake. Leave in the cooler, or a cool spot while you plan all the other things.
2. Carry a container of water to the bubble, add the carrots and parsnips and cook for 5 mins. Channel and put away to get dry somewhat. Heat the oil and 1 tbsp of the margarine in your skillet and cook the cut shallots and ground parsnips for 1-2 mins over a medium-high heat until simply beginning to brown, at that point add a decent sprinkle of water to the container, mix to scrape up any brown pieces, turn the heat down marginally, cover and cook for 4-5 mins, blending occasionally. The parsnips ought to be delicate. Add the spices and garlic and cook for one more moment, at that point tip into a bowl, scratching out also as you can. Season a little and put away.
3. Add the sugar and vinegar to the dish and bring to the bubble. Cook for a couple of moments until sweet, at that point mix in the

excess spread. Put away to cool marginally, at that point orchestrate the vegetables in the skillet, fanning them out. Top with the herby shallot and parsnip combination, driving it into any spaces there might be. Lay the baked good over the highest point of the vegetables and push in the edges a bit. Spot in the oven and heat for 30-35 mins until puffed and profound brilliant brown.

4. While the tart heats, put the nuts, sugar and spread in a little skillet with a touch of salt. Cook over a medium-high heat for around 5 mins, blending, until the sugar has disintegrated and covered the nuts. Add the rosemary for the latest possible time. Tip out onto a piece of preparing material and leave to cool for a couple of moments.

5. When the tart is prepared, eliminate from the oven and cautiously turn out onto a serving board. Scratch out any pieces that are left in the tin and add back to the tart. Slam the nuts to split them up and disperse over, alongside the disintegrated cheddar.

11. Griddled vegetables

Prep:10 mins Cook:25 mins Easy Serves 2

Ingredients:
- 1 large aubergine
- ½a lemon , zested and squeezed
- 3cloves of garlic , 1 squashed, 2 chopped
- 2 tbsp chopped parsley , in addition to extra to serve
- 1 tsp additional virgin olive oil , in addition to a little for showering
- 4 tsp omega seed blend (see tip)
- 2 tsp thyme leaves
- 1 tbsp rapeseed oil
- 1 red pepper , deseeded and cut into quarters
- 1 large onion , thickly cut
- 2 courgettes , cut on the point
- 2 large tomatoes , each cut into 3 thick cuts
- 8 Kalamata olives , split

Strategy:
1. Barbecue the aubergine, turning every now and again, until delicate all finished and the skin is rankled, around 8-10 mins. Then again, on the off chance that you have a gas hob, cook it straight ludicrous. At the point when it is sufficiently cool to deal with, eliminate the skin, finely hack the fragile living creature and

blend in with the lemon juice, 1 chopped clove garlic, 1 tbsp parsley, 1 tsp additional virgin olive oil and the seeds. Blend the leftover parsley in with the excess chopped garlic and the lemon zing.

2. In the interim, blend the thyme, squashed garlic and rapeseed oil and throw with the vegetables, keeping the onions as cuts as opposed to separating into rings. Heat a large frying pan dish and burn the vegetables until delicate and set apart with lines – the tomatoes will require the least time. Heap onto plates with the aubergine purée and olives, sprinkle over some additional olive oil and dissipate with the parsley, lemon zing and garlic.

Formula TIPS

OMEGA SEED MIX

This and a portion of different recipes in the Summer 2018 Healthy Diet Plan incorporate seeds to give protein and fundamental omega unsaturated fats. To make the omega seed blend, join 3 tbsp every one of sesame, sunflower and pumpkin seeds, at that point store in a container and use as proposed.

12. Vegetable tagine with apricot

Preparation and cooking time Prep:30 mins Cook:45 mins Easy Serves 4
Ingredients:

- For the tagine
- 1 tsp coconut oil or olive oil
- 1 red onion , chopped
- 2 garlic cloves , squashed
- ½ butternut squash (500g), chopped into large lumps
- 2 red peppers , chopped
- 400g can chickpeas , depleted
- 400g can chopped tomatoes
- 500ml veggie lover vegetable stock (like Marigold Vegan Bouillon Powder)
- 1 tsp ground cinnamon
- 1 tsp ground cumin
- 2 tsp turmeric
- 2 tsp paprika
- little bundle coriander , chopped
- little bundle mint , chopped, in addition to extra to serve
- pomegranate seeds , to serve (optional)

- For the apricot quinoa
- 280g quinoa
- 80g dried apricots , chopped
- 20g chipped almonds , toasted
- For the dressing
- 4 tbsp tahini
- 2 tsp protected lemon , finely chopped, in addition to 2 tsp fluid from the container
- 6 tbsp almond milk

Technique:

1. Heat the oil in a large griddle and fry the onion over a medium heat for 3 mins. Add the garlic and butternut squash, and cook for a further 7 mins.
2. Add the leftover vegetables and keep on fricasseeing for 3 mins prior to adding the chickpeas, tomatoes and stock, alongside the flavors and preparing. Stew for 30 mins, uncovered. In the interim, put 750ml water in a little pan, bring to a stew, at that point add the quinoa and cook for 20 mins. When cooked, mix in the apricots and almonds, in addition to a touch of salt.
3. To make the tahini dressing, whisk together every one of the ingredients in a little bowl. Season with a touch of salt.
4. Serve the quinoa with the tagine, and shower the tahini dressing over the top. Dissipate over some chopped coriander and mint and the pomegranate seeds, if using, to wrap up.

13. Smoked tofu vegan burger

Prep:35 mins Cook:5 mins Easy Serves 4

Ingredients:
- vegetable oil , for searing
- For the burger
- 1 yam (200g), stripped and cut into little lumps
- 1 tbsp olive oil
- 1 little onion , finely chopped
- 1 garlic clove , squashed
- 1 tsp cumin
- 1 tsp smoked paprika
- 1 tsp garlic salt
- 225g pack smoked tofu (we utilized The Tofoo Co.)
- 50g simmered cashews
- For the covering
- 1 tsp English mustard
- 150ml soy milk
- 75g plain flour
- 50g panko breadcrumbs
- 1 tsp garlic salt

- ½ tsp cayenne pepper
- 1 tbsp icing sugar

- 1 tsp heating powder
- For the slaw
- ¼ red cabbage , finely shredded
- 1 carrot , ground
- 2 tbsp chopped coriander
- ½ lime , squeezed
- 2 tsp sesame seeds
- To serve
- vegetarian mayonnaise (we utilized Rubies in the Rubble) blended in with ½ tbsp Sriracha
- vegetarian burger buns , divided and toasted

Technique:

1. Put the yam in a microwaveable bowl, cover with stick film and cook on high for 3 mins until delicate. Heat the oil in a non-stick griddle and fry the onion with a major spot of salt until delicate, around 5 mins. Add the garlic and flavors and cook for 2 mins more, at that point put away. Rush the tofu with the cashews in a blender, at that point tip in the yam and seared onions. Season and barrage again until joined. Shape into four burger patties and put away in the cooler on a lined heating plate while you make the slaw.

2. Make the slaw by joining the ingredients in a bowl, at that point put away until required. At the point when you're prepared to broil the patties, blend the mustard in with the soy milk in one bowl, at that point blend the leftover covering ingredients in another bowl. Thusly,

take every patty and plunge into the flour combination, at that point into the soy milk blend, at that point once again into the flour blend. Rehash this so you get a truly decent outside on the patties.

3. Empty the vegetable oil into a large griddle over a medium-high heat - you need the oil to come about 2cm up the side of the skillet. Once hot, utilize a spatula to painstakingly add the patties and tenderly fry for 1 min on each side until fresh, at that point leave to deplete on kitchen paper. Serve the burgers in burger buns, finished off with the slaw and sprinkled with the mayo.

14. Sesame & spring onion stir-fried udon with crispy tofu

Prep:5 mins Cook:15 mins Easy Serves 4

Ingredients:

- 400g square firm tofu
- 1 tbsp cornflour
- ½ - 1 tsp bean stew pieces, to taste
- ¼-½ tsp Szechuan peppercorns, ground, to taste
- 1 tbsp vegetable oil
- pack of spring onions, managed and cut into lengths
- 200g green beans, managed and cut into lengths
- 400g prepared to-utilize thick udon noodles
- ½ tbsp sesame oil
- 2 tsp sesame seeds, in addition to a squeeze to serve
- 1 tbsp low-salt soy sauce, in addition to extra to serve
- 1 tbsp rice vinegar

Technique:
1. Channel and wipe the tofu off with kitchen paper. Cut into solid shapes, enclose by more kitchen paper, and spot a weighty board over the top. Leave to deplete for 15 mins.
2. Blend the cornflour, stew chips and ground peppercorns together in a bowl with a spot of salt, at that point add the depleted tofu. Throw well to cover.
3. Heat a large portion of the vegetable oil in a large non-stick skillet over a high heat, and fry the tofu pieces for 5-6 mins until brilliant all finished. Scoop out of the dish, and leave to deplete on kitchen paper.
4. Add the leftover oil to the skillet and pan fried food the spring onions and beans for 3-4 mins until delicate and softly brilliant. Pour a pot of bubbling water over the noodles in a strainer to relax. Channel well, at that point tip into the dish. Fry for a couple of moments until quite hot. Add the sesame oil and sesame seeds, and sizzle for a couple of moments. Sprinkle in the soy sauce, rice vinegar, at that point add the tofu. Throw well, at that point serve in bowls with a spot of sesame seeds on top and more soy sauce as an afterthought.

Formula TIPS

MAKE INSTANT UDON NOODLE SOUP

Pour hot vegetable stock over any extra sesame and spring onion pan-seared udon with fresh tofu to cover. Mix through some miso paste, or additional soy sauce. Sprinkle over additional Szechuan peppercorns to serve.

15. Salt & pepper tofu

Prep:15 mins Cook:20 minsplus pressing
Easy Serves 4

Ingredients:
- 396g pack firm tofu
- 2 tbsp cornflour
- 1 tsp Sichuan or dark peppercorns (or a combination of the two), ground to a powder
- 2 tbsp sunflower or vegetable oil
- 2 red peppers , cut
- ¼ broccoli head, cut into exceptionally little florets
- 100g beansprouts
- 2 tsp low-salt soy sauce
- sesame oil , for sprinkling
- small bunch of coriander , leaves picked

Strategy:
1. Channel the tofu, wrap freely in kitchen paper and put on a plate. Rest a cleaving load up on top. In case you're using a light cleaving load up, burden it a few jars – a heavier hacking load up will be adequate all alone. Leave for 10-20 mins until the fabric feels wet from the

abundance fluid. Squeezing the tofu like this assists with giving it a firmer surface once cooked.

2. Slice the tofu down the middle down the middle like a book. Cut each piece into four triangles, as you would a piece of toast, at that point fifty-fifty again to give you 16 pieces altogether. Blend the cornflour, ground pepper and 1 tsp flaky ocean salt on a plate. Delicately turn each piece of tofu in the cornflour blend to cover.

3. Heat 1 tbsp oil in a wok. Sautéed food the peppers and broccoli for a couple of moments, to mollify a bit. Add the beansprouts and soy sauce. Cook for another 1-2 mins, ensuring the veg actually has a decent crunch. Sprinkle with a little sesame oil.

4. Heat the leftover sunflower oil in a large non-stick griddle and fry the covered tofu for 5 mins on each side until fresh. Serve on top of the vegetables, dissipated with the coriander.

16. Lighter vegetable lasagna

Prep:40 mins - 45 minsCook:1 hr and 15 mins
Easy Serves 4
Ingredients:

- For the meal vegetables
- 1 little aubergine , about 250g, cut into approx 3cm pieces
- 1 medium courgette , about 200g, cut into 2-3cm pieces
- 1 red pepper , deseeded and chopped into 2.5cm pieces
- 1 medium onion , split lengthways, cut into dainty wedges
- touch of stew drops
- 1 tbsp rapeseed oil
- For the pureed tomatoes
- 400g can plum tomatoes
- 1 medium carrot , chopped into little dice
- 3 garlic cloves , finely chopped
- 2 tbsp tomato purée (or sundried tomato purée – see tip)

- 400g can green lentils (with no additional salt), depleted
- 2 tbsp chopped basil , in addition to additional leaves to embellish
- For different layers
- 300g new spinach
- 1 medium egg
- 250g tub ricotta
- 1 adjusted tbsp chopped oregano , in addition to additional leaves to decorate
- great spot of ground nutmeg
- 9 dried lasagne sheets, each 17.5cm x 8cm
- 125g ball mozzarella , generally chopped
- 25g parmesan or vegan elective, ground
- 100g cherry tomatoes on the plant
- To serve
- green serving of mixed greens

Technique:

1. Heat oven to 220C/200C fan/gas 7. Put the aubergine, courgette, pepper and onion in a large, shallow cooking tin. Disperse with the stew drops and season with pepper and a touch of salt. Pour the oil over, throw together to cover (you can utilize your hands for this), at that point spread the vegetables out in a solitary layer. Cook for 15 mins, at that point give them a mix and spread them out once more. Cook for another 10-15 mins until softened and becoming brilliant.
2. While the vegetables are simmering, make the pureed tomatoes. Tip the tomatoes into a medium container, at that point empty 100ml water into the void can, whirl it adjust and fill

the pot. Add the carrot and garlic, and stew delicately for 20-25 mins, somewhat covered with the top and blending sporadically, until the carrot is simply delicate. Mix in the tomato purée and the lentils, season with pepper and stew for 2 mins more. Eliminate from the heat, mix in the basil and put away.

3. Tip the spinach into a large heatproof bowl, pour over bubbling water, press the leaves into the water and leave for 30 secs. Channel in a large colander and flush under chilly water momentarily to chill it off rapidly. Crush the spinach to eliminate the abundance water, at that point generally cleave. Beat the egg in a bowl and mix in the ricotta, oregano, nutmeg and some pepper.

4. Lay the lasagne sheets, spread well out, in a large shallow simmering tin and pour bubbling water over to cover. Move them around with a wooden spoon to ensure they aren't staying, at that point leave for 5 mins. ('No pre-cook' lasagne sheets profit by a concise drenching, which improves the surface and makes them more flexible for layering in the dish.) Drain well and quickly separate them out to forestall them staying.

5. At the point when the vegetables have got done with cooking, bring down the heat to 200C/180C fan/gas 6. Spread an extremely far layer of the pureed tomatoes (around 2 major spoonfuls) over the lower part of an ovenproof dish, around 25 x 18 x 7cm profound and 2 liters limit. Lay 3 lasagne sheets across the width of the dish and spread over portion of

the excess sauce and half of the simmered vegetables. Cover with 3 more lasagne sheets, at that point spread the spinach over the top and season with pepper. Put the ricotta blend on top in spoonfuls and spread out ludicrous. Cover with the last 3 lasagne sheets. Spread over the remainder of the pureed tomatoes and afterward the excess cooked vegetables. Disperse over the mozzarella and Parmesan to cover the vegetables and sauce however much as could reasonably be expected, at that point top with the cherry tomatoes. Season with pepper and lay a piece of foil freely preposterous. Can be made as long as a day ahead and chilled – permit an additional couple of mins when preparing the following day. Or on the other hand freeze for as long as multi month and defrost for the time being in the refrigerator.

6. Heat for 35 mins, at that point eliminate the thwart and prepare for a further 5-10 mins until everything is rising around the edges. Disperse with oregano and basil leaves, and present with a green plate of mixed greens.

Formula TIPS

WHAT IF I...

... utilized sundried tomato purée rather than customary tomato purée? The carbohydrate level would increment to 364 kcals. Absolute fat would ascend to 15.5g (immersed fat would remain something very similar).

HOW I MADE IT HEALTHIER

I decreased fat and immersed fat by simmering a portion of the veg in a base measure of rapeseed oil, which has less soaked fat than olive oil. Using less cheddar, and supplanting a velvety béchamel sauce with ricotta, implied that I cut the excess considerably further and decreased the measure of salt. I added additional veg, remembering cherry tomatoes for top and a layer of spinach, to add nutrient C and add to your 5-a-day. The lentils, spinach and aubergine assisted with expanding the fiber.

17. Italian vegetable soup

Preparation and cooking time Prep:15 mins Cook:55 mins Easy Serves 8

Ingredients:

- 2 every one of onions and carrots, chopped
- 4 sticks celery, chopped
- 1 tbsp olive oil
- 2 tbsp sugar
- 4 garlic cloves, squashed
- 2 tbsp tomato purée
- 2 narrows leaves
- hardly any twigs thyme
- 3 courgettes, chopped
- 400g can margarine beans, depleted
- 400g can chopped tomatoes
- 1.2l vegetable stock
- 100g parmesan or vegan same, ground
- 140g little pasta shapes
- little bundle basil, shredded

Technique:

1. Delicately cook the onion, carrots and celery in the oil in a large pan for 20 mins, until

delicate. Sprinkle in water in the event that they stick. Add the sugar, garlic, purée, spices and courgettes and cook for 4-5 mins on a medium heat until they brown a bit.

2. Pour in the beans, tomatoes and stock, at that point stew for 20 mins. In case you're freezing it, cool and do so now (freeze for as long as a quarter of a year). If not, add a large portion of the Parmesan and the pasta and stew for 6-8 mins until pasta cooked. Sprinkle with basil and remaining Parmesan to serve. Whenever frozen, thaw out then re-heat prior to adding pasta and cheddar and proceeding as above.

18. Spring vegetable orzo with broad beans, peas, artichokes & ricotta

Prep:25 mins Cook:30 mins More effort Serves 4

Ingredients:

- 150g orzo
- 1 lemon , zested and squeezed
- 4 tema, mammole or violet artichokes , or utilize jolted
- 5 tbsp additional virgin olive oil
- 150g new potatoes , like Jersey Royals, cut into reduced down pieces
- 5 spring onions or 4 infant leeks, meagerly cut
- 1 garlic clove , squashed
- 1 mint branch , in addition to 1 tbsp finely chopped mint
- 140ml white or rosé wine , or dry vermouth
- 300g expansive beans (podded weight)
- 200g new or frozen peas (podded weight, assuming new)
- 100g ricotta
- 1 tsp pink peppercorns , squashed

- pecorino or veggie lover elective, for grinding

Technique:
1. Bring a large pot of salted water to the bubble and cook the orzo adhering to pack guidelines until still somewhat firm. Channel, at that point quickly dive into cold water to end the cooking.
2. Divide the lemon, at that point cut the tips from the artichokes with a serrated blade and strip away the intense external leaves. Pare away any extreme pieces from the bases, and trim the stalks to about 5cm, stripping away the external skins to uncover the white centers. Quarter the artichokes, scooping out the shaggy stifles, at that point divide each quarter. Move to a bowl and press over the juice from a large portion of the lemon, throwing to cover.
3. Heat the oil in a hefty lined skillet over a medium heat and fry the potatoes, spring onions, garlic and artichokes, blending for 5-6 mins until the potatoes are beginning to brown. Add the mint twig, wine and 500ml water, at that point season, cover and stew for 12-15 mins until the potatoes and artichokes are delicate. Add the expansive beans and peas and cook for 2 mins more until delicate yet at the same time holding their splendid shading. Eliminate the skillet from the heat. Channel the orzo and mix into the skillet with the chopped mint and the vast majority of the lemon zing, at that point leave to a few minutes so the orzo can retain the flavors. Taste for preparing and change the salt, and

press over the leftover lemon half, on the off chance that you think it needs it.

4. Dish into warmed dishes and top with spoonfuls of the ricotta. Dissipate over the squashed pink peppercorns and the excess lemon zing, at that point grind over some pecorino to serve.

19. Summer vegetable & pesto rose tart

Prep:40 mins Cook:1 hr and 5 mins Serves 12

Ingredients:
- For the baked good
- 250g spelt flour
- 125g virus spread , cubed
- 25g gruyère (or veggie lover elective), finely ground
- 1 egg yolk , beaten
- For the filling
- 2 little yams , stripped
- 2 courgettes (1 green and 1 yellow looks pleasant)
- 1 little aubergine
- juice 1 little lemon
- 250g mascarpone
- 2 eggs
- 150g rocket pesto (make your own, or utilize a decent shop-got one)
- 25g new breadcrumbs

- 100g gruyère (or vegan elective), ground
- little bundle thyme , leaves picked
- 2 tbsp olive oil

Technique:

1. In the first place, make the cake. Tip the flour into a bowl with 1/2 tsp salt. Add the margarine and focus on using your fingertips until it takes after breadcrumbs. Mix through the cheddar with a cutlery blade. Add the egg yolk, shower more than 1 tbsp cold water, at that point utilize the blade to mix it in until bunches of mixture begin to shape. Tip onto a work surface and unite the mixture with your hands into a smooth ball. On the other hand, you can make the baked good in a food processor. Shape into a plate, enclose by stick film and chill for in any event 20 mins.

2. Using a mandolin or a sharp blade, cut the yams, courgettes and aubergines lengthways as meagerly as could really be expected. Brush the aubergine cuts with lemon juice as you go to keep them from becoming brown. Put the yam in a bowl with 2 tsp water, cover with stick film and cook in a microwave on high for 2 mins, at that point eliminate and leave to cool. Do likewise with the courgettes and aubergines, however cook for only 30 secs, at that point put away.

3. Remove the baked good from the ice chest and carry out to the thickness of a £1 coin. Line a 23cm fluted tart tin with the baked good. Trim the sides with some kitchen scissors, leaving a shade of about 1cm. Chill for another 10 mins.

Heat oven to 200C/180C fan/gas 6 and put a preparing plate on the center rack.

4. At the point when the baked good is cold and firm, line with heating material (scrunch it up first to make it more malleable), at that point load up with preparing beans. Prepare for 15 mins, at that point eliminate the beans and material and heat for 5 mins more until the cake is biscuity.

5. In the mean time, make the filling. Put the mascarpone, eggs, pesto, breadcrumbs and Gruyère in a bowl, season and blend well. Eliminate the baked good case from the oven, trim the sides with a little sharp blade so they're flush with the highest point of the tin, at that point spread the filling over the base.

6. Diminish oven to 180C/160C fan/gas 4. Channel any fluid from the vegetables, wipe off on kitchen paper, at that point season them all well. Stack a cut of yam, courgette and aubergine on top of one another at that point, beginning from one end, fold into a winding. Put in the tart. Layer up another three vegetable cuts, at that point wrap these around the spiraled veg in the middle. Proceed until the tart is full and you have made a rose impact. Sprinkle thyme leaves between the layers and shower the tart with oil.

7. Heat in the focal point of the oven for 40-45 mins until the vegetables are delicate and the filling has set. Eliminate from the oven and leave to cool in the tin for 15 mins prior to eliminating. Serve warm or cold.

20. potato dhal with curried vegetables

Prep:25 mins Cook:1 hr and 10 mins Easy Serves 4

Ingredients:

- 1 tbsp cold-squeezed rapeseed oil
- 1 medium onion , finely chopped
- 2 garlic cloves , meagerly cut
- 1 tbsp medium curry powder
- 200g dried split red lentils
- 500g yams , stripped and cut into lumps
- 2 tbsp lime (or lemon) juice in addition to lime wedges, to serve
- 100g full-fat regular bio yogurt
- coriander , to serve
- For the curried vegetables
- 100g green beans , managed and cut into off lengths
- 250g cauliflower , cut into little florets
- 2 medium carrots , cut
- 1 tbsp cold-squeezed rapeseed oil
- 1 medium onion , cut into meager wedges

- 2 garlic cloves , meagerly cut
- 1 tsp medium curry powder
- 200g ready tomatoes , generally chopped
- 1 long green bean stew , finely cut (deseeded on the off chance that you don't care for it excessively hot)

Technique:
1. To make the dhal, heat the oil in a large non-stick dish and fry the onion over a low heat for 10 mins, blending consistently, until softened and daintily browned – add the garlic for the last min. Mix in the curry powder and cook for 30 secs more.
2. Add the lentils, 1 tsp chipped ocean salt and 1 liter of water. Mix in the yams and bring to the bubble. Diminish the heat to a stew and cook the lentils for 50 mins or until the dhal is thick, blending routinely. Add a sprinkle of water if the dhal thickens excessively. Mix in the lime or lemon squeeze and season to taste.
3. While the dhal is cooking, make the curried vegetables. Half-fill a medium non-leave container with water and bring to the bubble. Add the beans, cauliflower and carrots, and get back to the bubble. Cook for 4 mins, at that point channel.
4. Return the skillet to the heat and add the oil and onion. Cook over a medium-high heat for 3-4 mins or until the onion is delicately browned, blending routinely. Add the garlic and cook for 1 min more until softened. Mix in

the curry powder and cook for a couple of secs, blending.

5. Add the tomatoes, green stew as indicated by taste and 200ml virus water. Cook for 5 mins or until the tomatoes are all around softened, mixing routinely. Mix in the whitened vegetables and cook for 4-5 mins or until hot all through. Season with dark pepper.

6. Split the dhal between four profound dishes and top with the curried vegetables. Present with the yogurt, coriander and lime wedges for pressing over.

Formula TIPS

Putting away LEFTOVERS

Freeze the dhal and vegetables in lidded cooler confirmation holders for as long as 3 months. Defrost for the time being then add a sprinkle of water and reheat until steaming hot all through.

21. Griddled vegetable tart

Prep:10 mins Cook:40 mins Easy Serves 4
Ingredients:
- 2 tbsp olive oil
- 1 aubergine , cut
- 2 courgettes , cut
- 2 red onions , cut into thick wedges
- 3 large sheets filo baked good
- 10-12 cherry tomatoes , divided
- sprinkle of balsamic vinegar
- 85g feta cheddar , disintegrated
- 1 tsp dried oregano
- large pack blended plate of mixed greens leaves and low-fat dressing, to serve

Technique:
1. Heat oven to 220C/200C fan/gas 7. Pop 33 x 23cm preparing plate in the oven to heat up. Brush an iron skillet with around 1 tsp of the oil and frying pan the aubergines until pleasantly scorched, at that point eliminate. Rehash with the courgettes and onions, using somewhat more oil on the off chance that you need to.

2. Eliminate the plate from the oven and brush with a little oil. Brush a large sheet of filo with oil, top with another sheet, add somewhat more oil and rehash with the last sheet. Move the baked good to the hot plate, driving it into the edges a bit.
3. Mastermind the griddled veg on top, at that point season. Add the tomatoes, cut-side up, at that point sprinkle on the vinegar and any excess oil. Disintegrate on the feta and sprinkle with oregano. Cook for around 20 mins until firm and brilliant. Present with the dressed blended plate of mixed greens leaves.

22. Mumsy's vegetable soup

Prep:10 mins Cook:30 mins Easy Serves 4
Ingredients:

- 200g sourdough bread, cut into bread garnishes
- 1 tbsp caraway seeds
- 3 tbsp olive oil
- 1 garlic clove, chopped
- 1 carrot, chopped
- 1 potato, chopped
- 600ml vegetable stock (we use bouillon)
- 100g cherry tomatoes, split
- 400g can chopped tomatoes
- touch of brilliant caster sugar
- 1 bouquet garni (2 sound leaves, 1 rosemary twig and 2 thyme branches integrated with string)
- 1 celery stick, chopped
- 200g cauliflower, cut into florets
- 150g white cabbage, shredded
- 1 tsp Worcestershire sauce

- 2 tsp mushroom ketchup

Strategy:
1. Heat oven to 180C/160C fan/gas 4. Put the bread on a preparing plate with the caraway seeds, a large portion of the oil and some ocean salt, and heat for 10-15 mins or until brilliant and fresh. Put away.
2. In the interim, heat the leftover oil in a large pan over a medium heat. Add the garlic, carrot and potato and cook for 5 mins, mixing as often as possible, until somewhat softened.
3. Add the stock, tomatoes, sugar, bouquet garni, celery and preparing and bring to a moving bubble. Diminish the heat, stew for 10 mins, at that point add the cauliflower and cabbage. Cook for 15 mins until the veg is delicate.
4. Mix in the Worcestershire sauce and mushroom ketchup. Eliminate the bouquet garni and serve the soup in bowls with the caraway bread garnishes.

23. Burmese tofu fritters (tohu jaw)

Prep:20 mins Cook:40 mins Plus cooling and setting Easy Serves 4-6

Ingredients:

- 2 tbsp vegetable oil , in addition to extra for the dish and fryer
- 100g gram flour
- ¼ tsp salt
- 1 tsp vegetable bouillon powder
- ¼ tsp ground turmeric
- ¼ tsp heating powder
- For the plunging sauce
- 1 ½ tbsp brilliant caster sugar
- 2 tbsp fish sauce
- 2 tbsp light soy sauce
- 2 limes , squeezed
- 2 finger chillies , cut into rings
- 3 garlic cloves , squashed

Technique:

1. Blend every one of the ingredients for the dunking sauce in a bowl. Cover and put away.
2. Oil a 15 x 20cm goulash dish. Put the flour, salt, bouillon powder, turmeric, heating powder and 350ml water in a large bowl and whisk completely. Cover and leave some place cool for 2 hrs, whisking incidentally.
3. Empty 250ml bubbling water into a large pan over a high heat. Add the oil, at that point pour in the flour combination and mix gradually with a large spoon. Diminish the heat to medium-high. Keep mixing for up to 10 mins until the blend begins to air pocket and structures a thick, custard-like consistency. Fill the goulash dish and leave at room temperature to set and cool totally.
4. Channel away any abundance fluid, envelop the tofu by kitchen paper and spot back in the dish. Now, you can cover and chill for up to 48 hrs until required.
5. At the point when you're prepared to broil the wastes, open up the tofu and cut it into 5 x 3 x 1cm square shapes.
6. Heat a wok or profound fat fryer with 5cm of oil (close to 33% full) until you can feel influxes of heat when you hold your hand 10cm over the fryer. Delicately lower 3 or 4 tofu square shapes into the hot oil – they should begin to sizzle nearly without a moment's delay. Fry for 3 mins until brilliant, at that point flip tenderly and fry for a further 3 mins. Eliminate with an opened spoon and channel in a colander set over a dish to get

abundance oil. Rehash with the following cluster.

7. At the point when you've singed all the tofu squanders, tip them back into the hot oil and fry for a further 4-5 mins for additional freshness. Channel the tofu squanders on a lot of kitchen paper and present with the garlic plunging sauce or a sweet bean stew sauce.

24. Smoky tofu tortillas

Prep:10 mins Cook:15 mins Easy Serves 4
Ingredients:

- 1 tbsp vegetable or olive oil
- 2 onions , each cut into 12 wedges
- 2 Romano peppers , deseeded and cut
- little pack coriander , leaves picked and stems finely chopped
- 2 tsp ground cumin
- 1 tsp hot smoked paprika
- 200g pack smoked tofu (I enjoyed Taifun), cut into reduced down pieces
- 400g can kidney beans , depleted and flushed
- 400g can cherry tomatoes
- 1 tbsp dull brown delicate sugar
- To serve
- 8 corn and wheat tortillas
- 2 limes , cut into wedges
- additional virgin olive oil , for sprinkling
- 1 large ready avocado , stoned, stripped and cut not long prior to serving
- thick yogurt or soured cream

Technique:
1. Heat the oil in a large griddle and add the onions and peppers. Season and cook on a high heat for 8 mins or until simply delicate and beginning to scorch. Add the coriander stems, fry for 1 min, blending, at that point add the flavors and cook for 2 mins more, mixing, until fragrant.
2. Tip in the tofu, beans, tomatoes and sugar, and cook for 5 mins until the sauce is very dry and the tofu is heated through. Warm the tortillas adhering to pack guidelines.
3. Taste the sauce for preparing and add the coriander leaves and a crush of lime. Sprinkle over some additional virgin olive oil and present with the tortillas, lime parts, avocado and yogurt or soured cream as an afterthought.

25. Miso roasted tofu with sweet potato

Prep:15 mins Cook:30 mins Easy Serves 2
Ingredients:
- 400g firm tofu , depleted
- 100g fine green beans
- 2 tbsp olive oil
- 2 tbsp dark or white sesame seeds , toasted
- 2 large yams
- 2 spring onions , finely cut
- For the dressing
- 3 tbsp white miso (in the event that you can't discover it, utilize 2 tbsp brown miso paste)
- 3 tbsp mirin
- 3 tbsp lime juice

Strategy:
1. Heat oven to 200C/180C fan/gas 6. Enclose the tofu by kitchen paper, place in a shallow dish and put a hefty plate on top to assist press with trip the water. At the point when the paper is wet, supplant with another wrapping and burden once more. Cleave the tofu into medium 3D squares (about 2.5cm).

In a little bowl, combine the dressing as one with a whisk.

2. Heat up the beans for 1 min, at that point channel, wash in chilly water and put away. Line a preparing plate with material, spread out the tofu and pour over a large portion of the dressing. Sprinkle the sesame seeds on top and blend well. Heat for 20-25 mins until brilliant and fresh. In the mean time, cut the yams down the middle, place in a bowl, cover with stick film and microwave for 10-15 mins until extremely delicate.

3. Crush the yam and serve in bowls with the tofu, green beans, the dressing poured over and some spring onions sprinkled on top.

26. Tofu brekkie pancakes

Preparation and cooking time Prep:10 mins Cook:10 mins Easy Serves 4 – 6

Ingredients:
- 50g Brazil nuts
- 3 cut bananas
- 240g raspberries
- maple syrup or nectar , to serve
- For the player
- 349g pack firm luxurious tofu
- 2 tsp vanilla concentrate
- 2 tsp lemon juice
- 400ml unsweetened almond milk
- 1 tbsp vegetable oil , in addition to 1-2 tbsp extra for broiling
- 250g buckwheat flour
- 4 tbsp light muscovado sugar
- 1 ½ tsp ground blended flavor
- 1 tbsp without gluten preparing powder

Strategy:
1. Heat oven to 180C/160C fan/gas 4. Disperse the nuts over a preparing plate and cook for 5

mins until hot and brilliant. Leave to cool, at that point hack. Turn the oven down low on the off chance that you need to keep the entire bunch of hotcakes warm, in spite of the fact that I think they are best enjoyed directly from the skillet.

2. Put the tofu, vanilla, lemon juice and 200ml of the milk into a profound container or bowl. Using a stick blender, mix together until fluid, at that point continue to go until it turns thick and smooth, similar to yogurt. Mix in the oil and the remainder of the milk to release the combination.

3. and rush to consolidate and circulate air through. In the event that there are any irregularities in the sugar, crush them with your fingers. Make a well in the middle, pour in the tofu combine and bring as one to make a thick hitter.

4. Heat a large (in a perfect world non-stick) griddle and twirl around 1 tsp oil. For brilliant hotcakes that don't stick, the dish and oil ought to be sufficiently hot to get an energetic sizzle on contact with the hitter, yet not so hot that it burns it. Test a drop.

5. Using a scoop or large serving spoon, drop in 3 spoonfuls of hitter, backing it out tenderly in the skillet to make hotcakes that are about 12cm across. Cook for 2 mins on the principal side or until bubbles fly over the vast majority of the surface. Extricate with a range blade, at that point flip over the hotcakes and cook for 1 min more or until puffed up and firm. Move to the oven to keep warm, in the event that you

need to, yet don't stack the hotcakes too intently. Cook the remainder of the player, using somewhat more oil each time. Serve warm with cut banana, berries, toasted nuts and a decent shower of maple syrup or nectar.

Conclusion

I would like to thank you for choosing this book
.Hope you liked all recipes within book. Alkaline diet
is mostly preferred by people who want to reduce
their weight. All recipes rae easy to prepare so try at
home and appreciate along with your family
members.
I wish you all good luck

9 781802 003208